AURORA BOREALIS
ALASKA'S NORTHERN LIGHTS

Photo © Hugh Rose

All Photography Provided by
Accent Alaska/Ken Graham Agency

Words cannot describe the magnificence of the natural phenomenon, northern lights. In 1621, the French scientist, Pierre Gassendi, referred to the magical lights as aurora borealis; Aurora, the Roman goddess of dawn, and Boreas, the god of the north wind. These colorful and luminous lights have intrigued humankind back to the days of Seneca and Aristotle. A variety of legends have associated them with omens of disaster, spirits of the dead, and merry dancers. The aurora is present in almost every area of the sky, but is usually too faint to be seen except near the north and south pole, (aurora australis), regions known as auroral ovals.

Three elements combine to create an aurora: sun particles, a magnetic force and gases. The aurora is caused by high-speed solar particles colliding with gases, mainly nitrogen and oxygen, in the atmosphere. The Earth's core, which is comprised of metals, acts as a giant magnet. The magnetic field prevents the solar wind from penetrating the Earth's atmosphere. Solar particles stream around the planet, encasing the Earth and its magnetic field within a comet-shaped cavity. Plunging into the atmosphere at 25 or more miles per second, the smallest particles are no bigger than grains of dust. The electrically charged particles glow similarly to a fluorescent tube. Earth's magnetic field forms them into beams. The light rays, which sway from side to side, are formed when the beams hit the atmosphere's gases. Each gas produces a particular color depending on the energy of the particle, whether or not it's ionized or neutral and how far it is from Earth. Red auroras are unique, occurring only during significant magnetic storms since red-oxygen reaction is very slow.

The aurora occurs at an altitude higher than the highest jet plane flies. Since the lowest sections of the aurora are 40 miles up, we only see a small part of the display from the Earth. They can reach elevations of 600 miles. The lights are the most impressive at times of magnetic storms and heightened sun spot activity. At this time solar flares erupt on the sun, thus, the atmosphere is hit with enormous amounts of solar particles. The number of sunspots increase and decrease in a pattern called the solar cycle. When the sunspots multiply, solar flares burst from the sun's surface. Millions of particles from the solar wind plunge into the atmosphere, creating sensational light shows. The solar cycles reach their peak every 11 years.

Denali National Park • Photo © Bob Butterfield

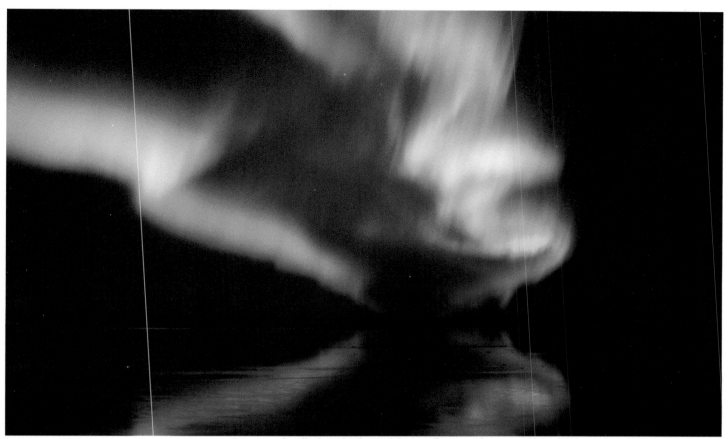

A spectacular display of color and form reflects on the water of Cook Inlet • Photo © Doug Crossley

The lights can range from a faint glow in the sky to a variety of dramatic formations. One's location relative to the aurora determines what is observed. Directly under the beams, the aurora would appear as bright rays of light shooting out in wavy motions. When viewed from farther away, they could appear like a huge shimmering curtain wrapping around the sky. When observed from a distance of 200 miles, north or south, they could appear as a huge ribbon of light, an arc reaching east to west. Usually, they cannot be seen until after midnight.

The state of Alaska along with the countries of Canada, Greenland, Iceland, Sweden, Denmark, Finland and Norway are the most likely places where you can observe the northern lights.

Like a bolt of lightning, this aurora seems to make contact with the Alaskan Range • Photo © Steve Nourse

A good example of a rare all-red auroral display • Photo © Mike Swanson

Brooks Range Aurora • Photo © Hugh Rose

An auroral form is reflected in a lake in the Alaskan interior • Photo © Greg Syverson

7

An auroral corona frames the Big Dipper • Photo © Hugh Rose

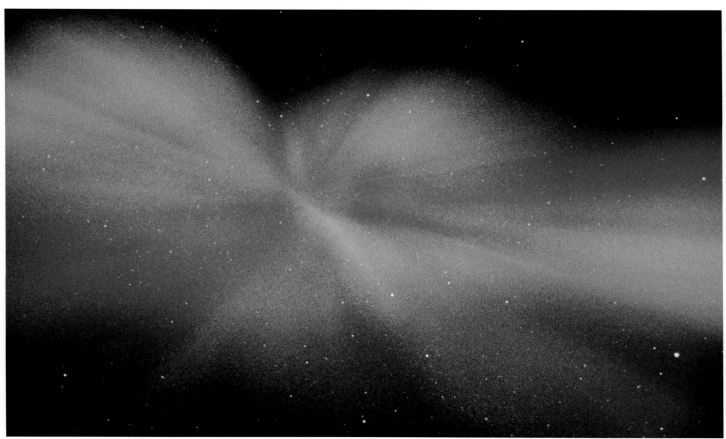

A rare corona aurora lights up the sky • Photo © Lee Davis

Northern lights with the Big Dipper • Photo © Ken Graham

A pink aurora borealis lights the sky near Cantwell, Alaska • Photo © Greg Syverson

The intensity of the northern lights turns almost white hot during an active display over the Seward Highway • Photo © Ken Graham

The northern lights beam down a circular display over the boreal forest • Photo © Steve Seiller

Breathing life into the winter night sky, the aurora illuminates above this frozen lake • Photo © Didier Lindsey

This aurora is in a linear display over the Chugach Range of Glacier Valley • Photo © Ken Graham

Interior Alaska with Mt. McKinley • Photo © Greg Syverson

A breathtaking display of lights over Anchorage • Photo © Mike Swanson

NATIONAL
PARK
SERVICE

DENALI
NATIONAL PARK AND PRESERVE

Abandoned gold dredge near Fairbanks • Photo © Hugh Rose

Travelers on Parks Highway stop for spectacular view of the aurora borealis • Photo © Steve Nourse

A dramatic auroral curtain with green, white and red colors mix in the swirling sky • Photo © Cary Anderson

Girdwood • Photo © Ken Graham

A corona aurora hangs like a curtain near Fairbanks • Photo © Lee Davis

Interior Alaska • Photo © Steve Nourse

An aurora, with brilliant hues of crimson red and white, illuminates the Alaskan interior night sky • Photo © Greg Syverson

Hale-Bopp Comet and aurora over the Chugach Mountain Range bordering Alaska's Knik River Valley • Photo © Cary Anderson

Hale-Bopp Comet appears to be entering the aurora, although they are actually millions of miles apart • Photo © Gene Jensen

Hale-Bopp Comet and a spectacular auroral display as seen over the Big River Delta • Photo © Gene Jansen

The aurora borealis creates a beautiful backdrop for this winter camping scene • Photo © Greg Syverson

The aurora sheds a green haze over the Knik River near Palmer • Photo © Mike Swanson

The northern lights dance above Cranberry Ridge in Denali National Park • Photo © Allen R. Kurkov

Sometimes resembling a bolt of lightning, the aurora borealis can be visible in cloudless skies during all seasons in Alaska.

Northern lights over Palmer, Alaska • Photo © Dorothy Keeler

The rare red aurora lights the night sky • Photo © Mike Swanson

Northern lights in the Brooks Range • Photo © Rolf Hicker

The northern lights light up the sky over Mt. Susitna near Anchorage • Photo © Sharon Walleen

Due to an effect of perspective, the end of the auroral curtain appears to rise like smoke from the ground at the horizon • Photo © Greg Syverson

An active auroral curtain partially blocks the light from a nearly full moon. • Photo © Greg Syverson

A fire crimson vertical curtain near Cantwell • Photo © Greg Syverson

The aurora borealis streams past a winter camping scene • Photo © Hugh Rose

Chugach Mountains • Photo © Greg Syverson

Red aurora, Chugach Mountains • Photo © Cary Anderson

Waves of green aurora wash over the sunset–lit sky of the Brooks Range • Photo © Hugh Rose

A colorful curtain of aurora appears to eminate from the chimney of a cabin near Fairbanks • Photo © Hugh Rose

Multihued aurora over Chugach Mountains • Photo © Ken Graham

Green northern lights over the Knik River • Photo © Cary Anderson and Tom Walker

Northern lights near the Glenn Highway • Photo © Dicon Joseph

Camping in the Talkeetna Mountains with the northern lights • Photo © Steve Nourse

This finger-like aurora soars over a mountainous region of the Brooks Range • Photo © Hugh Rose

Northern lights over Alaskan pipelines, North Slope • Photo © Greg Syverson

Northern lights above Knik River Valley and Chugach Mountains • Photo © Cary Anderson

The full moon competes in a contest of beauty with this aurora • Photo © Cary Anderson

Northern lights above a farm in Matanuska Valley • Photo © Cary Anderson

A rare multicolored red aurora seen over Pioneer Peak in the Matanuska-Susitna Valley • Photo © Didier J. Lindsey

Northern lights in the Alaskan interior night sky • Photo © Greg Syverson

Mt. McKinley and the Alaska Range under a beautiful auroral display • Photo © Greg Syverson

A beautiful green aurora undulates in the Brooks Range • Photo © Hugh Rose

Colorful curtains of aurora light the sky at sunset over the Endicott Mountains in the northern Brooks Range • Photo © Hugh Rose

Moonlight shares the night sky with a colorful aurora • Photo © Dorothy Keeler

Curtains of purple, red and green dance above a boreal forest • Photo © Hugh Rose

Northern lights in Denali Park • Photo © Tom Walker

Winter camping in Alaska • Photo © Mike Swanson

Vertical rays of aurora borealis over a cabin near Cantwell, Alaska • Photo © Greg Syverson